Paul Cookson lives in Retford with his wife and two children.

Since 1979 Paul has been publishing poetry. Since 1989 he has worked as a poet, visiting over a thousand schools to give performances and lead workshops. Since 1997 he has edited numerous poetry anthologies. Since 1973 he has been singing along with Slade's *Merry Xmas Everybody*. This anthology reflects all of these facts. It even includes the lyrics to that famous song. Paul is particularly pleased to have his work in the same collection as Slade's song as he is a lifelong fan of the group.

Jane Eccles is a prolific and talented illustrator. She lives in London with her husband, Graham, her son, Theo and her cat, Wilfred.

CHRISTMAS POEMS

Chosen by **Paul Cookson**

Illustrated by **Jane Eccles**

MACMILLAN CHILDREN'S BOOKS

~~Dedicated to~~ *Billy Baxter*
(and his mum and dad, Richard and Kate, too)

First published 2000 by Macmillan Children's Books
This edition produced 2001 for
The Book People Ltd,
Hall Wood Avenue,
Haydock, St Helens WA11 9UL

ISBN 330 392174

This collection copyright © Paul Cookson 2000
All poems copyright © the individual authors
Illustrations copyright © Jane Eccles 2000

The right of Paul Cookson to be identified as the
author of this work has been asserted by her in accordance
with the Copyright, Designs and Patents Act 1988.

579864

A CIP catalogue record for this book is available from the British Library.

Printed by Mackays of Chatham plc, Chatham, Kent

Lyrics of *Merry Christmas Everybody* published by kind permission of
Barn Publishing (Slade) Limited © 1973. Written by Neville Holder/James Lea.
'Letter from Egypt' by Moira Andrew first published in *Cambridge Contemporary Poets*,
CUP 1992. © Moira Andrew, 1992.

Contents

Caribbean Christmas

IT'S CHRISTMAS TIME	(CALL)
IT'S CHRISTMAS TIME	(RESPONSE)
EVERYBODY FEELS FINE	(CALL)
EVERYBODY FEELS FINE	(RESPONSE)
LET THE LIGHT SHINE	(CALL)
LET THE LIGHT SHINE	(RESPONSE)
FOR ALL MANKIND	(CALL)
FOR ALL WOMANKIND	(RESPONSE)

A cool tropical breeze
dances with the trees
the palms trees are swaying
the sweet music is playing
outside people basking in the golden sun
it's Christmas time there's hope for everyone.

In the Caribbean celebrations fill the air
it's Christmas time it happens once a year
a righteous king is born a religious affair
an important day for the world to share.

Jonkonnu dancers parading through the streets
To the reggae, calypso and the West African beats
Yam and banana, sorrel, ginger beer
Fireworks exploding loud and clear.

IT'S CHRISTMAS TIME	(CALL)
IT'S CHRISTMAS TIME	(RESPONSE)
EVERYBODY FEELS FINE	(CALL)
EVERYBODY FEELS FINE	(RESPONSE)
LET THE LIGHT SHINE	(CALL)
LET THE LIGHT SHINE	(RESPONSE)
FOR ALL MANKIND	(CALL)
FOR ALL WOMANKIND	(RESPONSE)

The Christmas market conjures up a variety of
    flavours
with all the Christmas trimmings for the folks to
    savour
the girls and boys making plenty of noise
when they visit the market to choose their toys.

Santa Claus visits the Caribbean
to get a suntan before he visits England
he has a long white beard and a bright red suit
a bobble on his hat and he wears big black boots.

A smiling face with a warm embrace
breeds a joyful race for a peaceful place
a peaceful world is what we need
not a world filled with hate, war and greed.

IT'S CHRISTMAS TIME	(CALL)
IT'S CHRISTMAS TIME	(RESPONSE)
EVERYBODY FEELS FINE	(CALL)
EVERYBODY FEELS FINE	(RESPONSE)
LET THE LIGHT SHINE	(CALL)
LET THE LIGHT SHINE	(RESPONSE)
FOR ALL MANKIND	(CALL)
FOR ALL WOMANKIND	(RESPONSE)

So goodwill to everyone on this spiritual day
let Jah light shine to guide our way
let your heart shine light like a feather
and let PEACE, LOVE and HARMONY bind us
    together.

IT'S CHRISTMAS TIME   (CALL)
IT'S CHRISTMAS TIME   (RESPONSE)
EVERYBODY FEELS FINE   (CALL)
EVERYBODY FEELS FINE   (RESPONSE)
LET THE LIGHT SHINE   (CALL)
LET THE LIGHT SHINE   (RESPONSE)
FOR ALL MANKIND   (CALL)
FOR ALL WOMANKIND   (RESPONSE)

Levi Tafari

Letter from Egypt

Dear Miriam,
Just a line
to let you know how things
are with us and of course to
thank you (and your good man)
for all you did for us – and
at your busiest time too
what with the census and
everything. I was quite
exhausted and the baby was
beginning to make himself
felt. If it hadn't been
for your help that night
my baby might have died.

Good of you
to put up with all our
visitors – who'd have
thought, six scruffy
shepherds up and leaving
their sheep like that?
Still they were good-
hearted and they meant well.
I hope they brought some
extra trade to the inn.
They looked in need of
a hot drink and a meal.

And what about
those kings, Miriam? Kneeling
there in their rich robes
and all? And me in nothing but
my old blue dress! Joseph
said not to worry, it was
Jesus they'd come to see.
Real gentlemen *they* were.
But what funny things to
give a baby – gold and myrrh
and frankincense. That's men
all over! It wouldn't cross
their minds to bring a shawl!

Sorry we left
so suddenly. No time for
goodbyes with King Herod on
the warpath! We had to take
the long way home and I'm so
tired of looking at sand!
Joseph has picked up a few
jobs mending this and that so
we're managing quite well.
Jesus grows bonnier every
day and thrives on this way
of life, but I can't wait
to see Nazareth again.

Love to all
at the inn,

    Mary

Moira Andrew

Wanted

WANTED – a reliable star
to lead small party
westwards. Bright with
good sense of direction.
Wage dependent on
experience. Send CV to
Wiseman, CHILDWATCH.

Sue Cowling

Curse of the Mistletoe

I stand beneath the mistletoe
and dream of kissing Mary
but all I get is Gran
and her nostrils that are hairy.

Paul Cookson

Stables

Stables are unhealthy places,
not somewhere you are likely to invite a friend or posh
   company
for a quiet chat and a cup of tea.

Stables are dirty places,
containing vast amounts of straw,
covering vast amounts of dung and droppings
which doesn't smell that good really.

Stables are places
you would expect to find animals inhabiting.
Animals such as horses, donkeys, cows,
sheep, geese, hens, ducks,
rats, mice, fleas, spiders, lice
and lots of other messy things.

Stables are not quiet places,
but places of whinnying, braying, mooing,
bleating, cackling, clucking, quacking,
squeaking, scratching, buzzing and general confusion.

All in all, stables are pretty unhealthy places,
not really somewhere you would expect a child to be
   born,
never mind a king.

Paul Cookson

The Snore Directory

When shooting through the sky
and dipping right down low,
have you ever wondered
how Santa knows which way to go?

It's not because he's magic
or can work out left from right,
it's not because he's got radar
to guide him through the night.

No, Santa always finds his way
down to your front door,
by listening to the gentle sound
of your grumbling, guiding snore.

For no two snores are quite the same,
they all have a special beat;
some are long and very loud –
others short and sweet.

So if you want Santa to call
make sure you're up in bed,
or he won't be able to hear you
and go somewhere else instead.

Andrew Collett

For Brownie (the goldfish)

For Brownie
(the goldfish)
– this Christmas
I bought –
a friend to play with.
But, since Mr Piranha arrived,
I have not seen Brownie.
I expect they are playing
hide and seek.

Peter Dixon

Advent Calendar

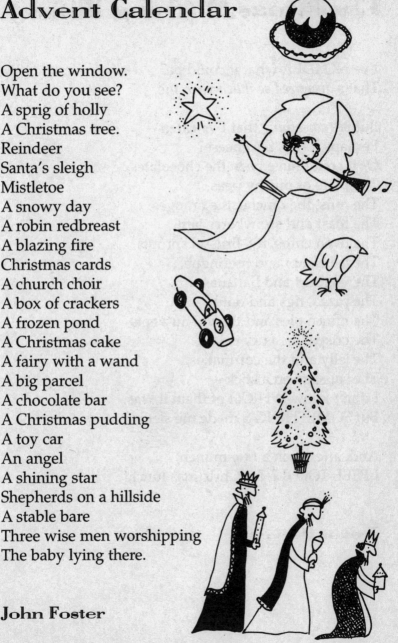

Open the window.
What do you see?
A sprig of holly
A Christmas tree.
Reindeer
Santa's sleigh
Mistletoe
A snowy day
A robin redbreast
A blazing fire
Christmas cards
A church choir
A box of crackers
A frozen pond
A Christmas cake
A fairy with a wand
A big parcel
A chocolate bar
A Christmas pudding
A toy car
An angel
A shining star
Shepherds on a hillside
A stable bare
Three wise men worshipping
The baby lying there.

John Foster

Christmas Morning Blues

I've NO IDEA what it could be
That's *disagreed so much* with me.

But it's *something* that I've eaten –
Perhaps it was the cheese?
Or it could have been the chocolates,
The plate of mushy peas,
The nuts, the quiche, the oranges,
The toast and strawberry jam,
The oven chips, the Brussel sprouts,
The ice cream and meringue,
The yoghurt and bananas,
The pizza, figs and dates,
The mince pies and the vol-au-vents,
The crisps, the fairy cakes,
The jelly and the cornflakes,
The sausage on a stick –
I don't know WHICH of them it was,
But SOMETHING'S made me sick!

And, after such a *tiny* munch,
I FEEL TOO ILL for Christmas lunch!

Trevor Harvey

Merry Xmas Everybody

Are you hanging up a stocking on your wall
It's the time that every Santa has a ball
Does he ride a Red Nose Reindeer
Does a ton up on his sleigh
Do the fairies keep him sober for a day –

So here it is Merry Christmas
Everybody's having fun
Look to the future now
It's only just begun

Are you waiting for the family to arrive
Are you sure you've got the room to spare inside
Does your Granny always tell ya
That the old songs are the best
Then she's up and Rock 'n' Rollin' with the rest

So here it is Merry Christmas
Everybody's having fun
Look to the future now
It's only just begun

What will your Daddy do
When he sees your Mamma kissing Santa Claus
Ah ah . . .

Are you hanging up a stocking on your wall
Are you hoping that the snow will start to fall
Do you ride on down the hillside
In a buggy you have made
When you land upon your head then you bin sleighed

So here it is Merry Christmas
Everybody's having fun
Look to the future now
It's only just begun

So here it is Merry Christmas
Everybody's having fun
Look to the future now
It's only just begun

It's Christmas . . .

Neville Holder / James Lea

The Christmas Pudding – From Start to Finish!

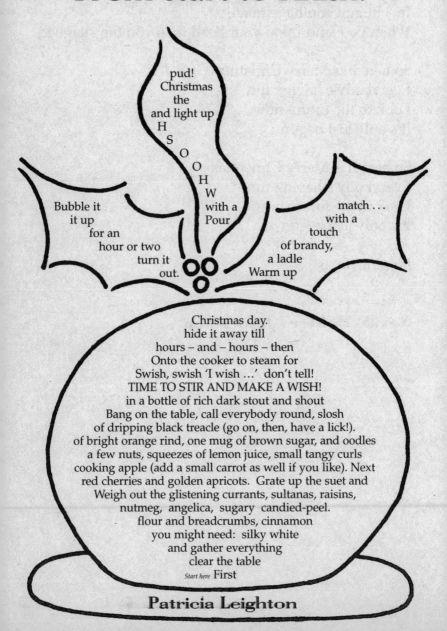

pud!
Christmas
the
and light up
H
S
O
O
H
W
with a
Pour

Bubble it
it up
for an
hour or two
turn it
out.

match ...
with a
touch
of brandy,
a ladle
Warm up

Christmas day.
hide it away till
hours – and – hours – then
Onto the cooker to steam for
Swish, swish 'I wish ...' don't tell!
TIME TO STIR AND MAKE A WISH!
in a bottle of rich dark stout and shout
Bang on the table, call everybody round, slosh
of dripping black treacle (go on, then, have a lick!).
of bright orange rind, one mug of brown sugar, and oodles
a few nuts, squeezes of lemon juice, small tangy curls
cooking apple (add a small carrot as well if you like). Next
red cherries and golden apricots. Grate up the suet and
Weigh out the glistening currants, sultanas, raisins,
nutmeg, angelica, sugary candied-peel.
flour and breadcrumbs, cinnamon
you might need: silky white
and gather everything
clear the table
Start here First

Patricia Leighton

Christmas Decoration

o
o
o
o
o
o
o
hhh!
it's not much
fun as a Christmas
decoration – I only work
one month a year and then
for the other eleven months
I'm stuffed into a box next
to old goody-two-shoes
the fairy – what a
life eh?!

James Carter

All of Us Knocking on the Stable Door

Three great kings, three wise men
Tramp across the desert to Bethlehem
Arrive at the inn, don't travel no more
they start knocking at the stable door.

Knocking at the door, knocking at the door
All of us are knocking at the stable door.

I've got myrrh, he's got gold
He's got frankincense and all of us are cold
We stand here shivering, chilled to the core
We're just knocking on the stable door.

The star above it glows in the sky
Burning up the darkness and we know why
A baby King's asleep in the straw
So we start knocking on the stable door.

Travelled some distance, we've travelled far
Melchior, Casper and Balthazaar
We are so wealthy, the baby's so poor
But here we are knocking on the stable door.

Now is the time, now is the hour
To feel the glory, worship the power
We quietly enter, kneel on the floor
Just the other side of the stable door.

Knocking on the door, knocking on the door
All of us knocking at the stable door.

Knocking on the door, knocking on the door
We're all knocking on the stable door.

David Harmer

Letter to Santa

With Christmas fast approaching
I thought you'd like to know
Just how I've been behaving,
Through the year till now.
                    (In case it makes a difference)

I thought I ought to point out
That I was not to blame,
When someone left the gate undone
And our dog ran off down the lane.
                    (He's an expert at escaping, anyway)

Then the tap was left turned on,
When the plug was in the sink,
I didn't mean to cause a flood,
I only went to get a drink.
                    (I was half asleep at the time)

And when salt got in the sugar bowl
Mum put it in her tea,
I've no idea why everyone
Assumed that it was me.
                    (The kind of mistake anyone could make)

Then when Grandpa lost his new false teeth
My sister found them in her bed,
Well, if you'd heard the way she screamed
Your face would turn red!
            (Doesn't mean I was guilty)

When I forgot to take my muddy shoes off,
When I came in through the door,
How was I to know that they
Had new carpet on the floor?
            (I'd only been playing football)

So Santa, thought I'd let you know,
Though things have gone a little wrong,
I've really tried hard to be good,
But – a year's so long!
    (I'll try harder next year, promise!)

With love from Darren.

Anne Logan

A Naughty Boy Tale

A boy I know called Sammy Day
once discovered Santa's sleigh
parked beside a Christmas tree
– whilst Santa went to have some tea.
Sam looked around – and by the door
he spied a sack upon the floor:
'His present sack!' he cried in glee!
'That's just the sort of thing for me!'
and with a laugh and a robber's shout
he took it home to sort it out.
'What a prize!' he grinned in glee.
'Lots of presents all for me!'
and with a shake of bag and head,
he emptied it upon his bed.
'Oh no!' he gasped
– oh, what a shock –
piles of pants
and vest and socks
smelly trainers
an old red coat
a bobble hat
and powdered soap.

A note inside

'To dearest Sam
Wash and dry these
if you can.

love Santa'

Peter Dixon

I'm Making a Hat for the Christmas Party

I'm
making
a hat for the
Christmas party
everyone makes a hat
but mine always seem to go lop-sided

Coral Rumble

A Question at Christmas

Are
all
the
chim-
neys
get-
ing
thin-
ner,
dear?

Or do I eat
more dinner
every year?

Sue Cowling

Claustrophobia

Emily's got claustrophobia
She's afraid of Santa Claus
Christmas is different in her house
It's not like in mine or yours

She's terrified of men with beards
And suits of brightest red
Sneaking down the chimney
While she's fast asleep in bed

She's hidden away her stockings
At the back of the chest of drawers
She's covered up the fireplace
And locked the bedroom door

A kiss from Father Christmas
Is the thing she dreads the most
She'd rather be hugged by Dracula
Or Jacob Marley's ghost

She hates holly, robins and ivy
She won't go and play in the snow
You'll never catch her standing
Beneath the mistletoe

Emily's got claustrophobia
Carol singers make her feel queer
Don't wish her a Merry Christmas
She's hiding away till New Year.

Adrian Henri

Nowhere to Move!

At Christmas time there's Amy and Bill,
Both the twins and Auntie Gill,
Polly and Peter and Uncle Paul.
There's nowhere to move and everywhere's full.

3

At Christmas time there's Amy and Bill,
Both the twins and Auntie Gill,
Polly and Peter and Uncle Paul.
The mugs are all dirty, the sink is blocked,
The bathroom's in use and the toilet's locked.
There's nowhere to move and everywhere's full.

At Christmas time there's Amy and Bill
Both the twins and Auntie Gill,
Polly and Peter and Uncle Paul,
There's Mac and Sam and Ann and Dan,
Amy's gran and Ann's new man.
The mugs are all dirty, the sink is blocked,
The bathroom's in use and the toilet's locked.
There's nowhere to move and everywhere's full.

At Christmas time there's Amy and Bill
Both the twins and Auntie Gill,
Polly and Peter and Uncle Paul,
There's Mac and Sam and Ann and Dan,
Amy's gran and Ann's new man.
The mugs are all dirty, the sink is blocked,
The bathroom's in use and the toilet's locked.
I can't find my toothbrush, I can't find my comb,
I can't find my gerbil, I can't find my mum!
There's nowhere to move but . . . I'll be sad when
    they've gone.

Trevor Millum

The Christmas Eve News

Good Evening

The police authorities are hopeful that tonight they
will finally get to the bottom of their longest-standing
unsolved mystery – the case of the serial present-giver
Father Christmas, also known as Santa Claus.
Inspector Hunch of Scotland Yard said that the police
have, with the use of an advanced computer program,
found a pattern to the break-ins by this intruder and
are confident that he will strike again tonight.
Inspector Hunch went on to add that members of the
public should not be unduly alarmed by the likelihood
of a break-in and stressed that although the strange
intruder always leaves gifts he has never been known
to take anything other than the odd mince pie and a
tipple from the liquor cabinet.

To assist the police with this investigation, in shopping
centres all over the country reconstructions have been
staged with the help of Father Christmas lookalikes
performing the act of giving. It is hoped that these
reconstructions might jog the memories of members of
the public with any information which might help
unmask the mystery giver.

Father Christmas is described as tallish, heavily bearded and athletic, although overweight. He is said to dress in a red suit and matching bobble hat. The police advise members of the public who witness Father Christmas in the act of leaving gifts in their bedrooms to pretend to be asleep but urged them to phone Scotland Yard as soon as the intruder has left the scene of the generosity.

Now the Christmas Eve weather. Under tonight's brightly shining moon, deep snow is expected of the crisp and even kind. A cruel frost is expected later.

That is the end of the news.

Wishing you a safe and Merry Christmas.

Goodnight.

Philip Waddell

Christmas Eve

I'm trying to sleep on Christmas Eve
but I really can't settle down,
and I don't want to lie
with wide open eyes
till the morning comes around.

I hear Mum and Dad downstairs,
doing their best to keep quiet,
and although I'm in bed
with my favourite ted,
in my head there's a terrible riot.

I'm thinking of Christmas morning
and all the presents I'll find,
but what if I've missed
something good off my list,
it keeps going round in my mind.

Mum has been baking all day
making rolls, mince pies and cake,
and I know quite well
it's this heavenly smell
that's keeping me wide awake.

Perhaps I'll slip down for some water
though I ought to stay in my room,
but maybe I'll risk
a slap with the whisk
for a lick of Mum's mixing spoon.

If I had just one mince pie
then I know it would be all right,
fast asleep,
not another peep,
my eyes shut tightly all night.

Now Dad says Father Christmas
won't leave any presents for me.
Make no mistake,
if you're still awake,
he'll pass you by, you'll see!

But I've tried and I've tried and I've tried
and I keep rolling round in my bed,
I still can't sleep,
and I'm fed up with sheep
so I'm counting reindeer instead!

Brian Moses

... four hundred
and twenty two,
four hundred
and ...

While the Elves were Asleep

On December the twenty-third
Father Christmas got up early.

The elves were all snoring,
the reindeer asleep.

Father Christmas tiptoed to the bathroom,
turned on the light.

He looked at his face
in the mirror.

He put in the plug
and filled the sink.

He opened the cupboard
and took out the things.

Father Christmas got down to work
quietly, moving slowly.

The sun hauled itself up
with a yawn,

lighting up the bathroom mirror
and Father Christmas,

his big bald face
like a red balloon,

his beard in the sink,
his hair sticking up like a cockatoo's

in the biggest mohican you've ever seen.
Father Christmas started to spray it green.

Ian McMillan

Santa Clues

Father Christmas
had a problem

all his toys
were disappearing

*Who will help me
solve this mystery?*

We will, Santy!
cried the Sherlock-Gnomes.

Joan Poulson

It's a Christmas Tree

Someone stole my crisps.
Who?
No one knows.
It's a crisp mystery.

Nick Toczek

Rudolph's Story

Last night as we practised for Christmas
Old Santa got carried away
Looping the loop over Yorkshire
He fell right out of the sleigh.

We saw him float down through the sky
As the town far below lay asleep
We saw him open his parachute
Then land in a compost heap.

At last we found the right garden
All we saw were his boots in the air
It took him a time but he struggled free
With cabbage leaves stuck in his hair.

'I've lost all my keys!' he shouted.
'From my pocket during my fall
The keys that open the workshop door
We won't have a Christmas at all!'

We started to dig through the compost
The terrible smell made us sneeze
We jumped a mile when a little voice said,
'Please, are you looking for these?'

She stood there holding some keys
They glowed with Santa's power
'I'm Sally,' she said, 'here take them back
Then Santa, please have a shower!'

He clapped his hands and cried, 'Thank you
Now I can fill up my sack
I tell you what, Sally, for a reward
Jump onto Rudolph's back.'

She felt as light as a snowflake
You should've heard us all yell
We zoomed past the stars, halfway to Mars
Happy, in spite of the smell.

On Christmas Eve we found Sally
Fast asleep in her bed
We left her a sack bursting with presents
And a note from Santa which said,

'Dear Sally, you really saved Christmas
It wasn't some wonderful dream
From all of us here, we'll see you next year
Welcome to Santa's team!'

David Harmer

A Kitten for Christmas

Day One he sneaked into the fridge,
Enjoyed a turkey tea.

Day Two he knocked the sparkly stars
Down from the Christmas tree.
Day Three he fancied streamers,
Went swinging up and down.

Day Four the tinsel took his eye,
He scattered it around.
Day Five the flashing lights were chewed
And pulled on to the floor.

Day Six the holly ripped apart –
I couldn't take much more.

Day Seven was the fairy's turn,
Her lovely dress so tattered.

Day Eight her wand was rather bent
And baubles bright were shattered.
Day Nine we threatened banishment
If havoc did not stop.
Day Ten he purred and looked so cute
Was pardoned on the spot.

Eleven gone and Christmas cards
Were torn up in a trice.

Twelfth Night, we breathed a sigh at last –
He started chasing mice.

Hilary Tinsley

Christmas Cards

Merry Christmas Son,
And a well-beha ved New year-
Any more cheek from you,
And you'll be out on your ear!

Dad

★ ★ ★ ★ ★ ★ ★
Hands-off Christmas, Brother!
Remember, my stuff's mine!
If you dare touch my presents
I'll make you pay a fine.
YOUR BIG SISTER

To Myself,
Have an absolutely
WICKED Christmas!!!!

Merry
Yuletide
Grandson!
Have a lovely
But I'll want a
To keep out of
day,
rest, so do your best
Grandma
my way.

Good tidy-ings, dear Son,
And do be nice and tidy!
Keep your litter off my glitter
Or it'll spoil my Christmas Day!

Mum
xxx

Kate Williams

The Visitors

'You must both be very proud,'
smiled the first
weighing up the situation exactly.

'A bit dribbly, isn't he?'
observed the second accurately
but with a foolish grin.

'Coochie, coochie,' cooed the third playfully –
completely forgetting as he gazed at the child
to say anything wise.

Philip Waddell

Christmas Eve

☆

Our
pud is
cooked,
meat stuffed and rolled –
smells drift of fruit and almonds where
the cake is iced and waiting.

Our tree is up, green, red and gold,
and twists of tinsel shimmer there
from lights illuminating.

Our foil-wrapped secrets to unfold,
and tiptoe stockings hung with care,
are all at once creating,

A feeling that we want to hold
suspended in the tingling air –

**It's
called
anticipating.**

Liz Brownlee

Dear Santa

Dear Santa, when it's Christmas
and you finally appear
after all those weeks of waiting,
please don't give presents this year

to my dad because he tells me off
for swinging in my chair,
to my mum because it really hurts
when she runs a comb through my hair.

To my big brother Benjamin
who's awfully mean to me,
and to little sister Sara
who's on at me constantly.

To cousins Jill and Josephine
who are dreadful little pests,
and to my teacher at school
who sets such difficult tests.

To the rabbit who tries to bite
    me
and the crazy cat next door,
to the dog who lays in my way
so I trip and fall on the floor.

To the man across the road
who never smiles or waves,
and to my grumpy neighbour
who tells me to behave.

And please don't listen if they should say
that I deserve nothing too.
I know you won't believe them,
I've put my faith in you.

I'm always good and kind,
I'm careful and I'm clever,
and I'm never nasty to anyone,
not ever . . . !

Brian Moses

Who Drops Down the Chimney?

Cats get visits from Santa Paws
Sharks listen out for Santa Jaws
Crabs hope for gifts from Santa Claws
Crows' stockings are filled by Santa Caws

Footballers cheer for Santa Scores
Sailors sigh for Santa Shores
Judges wait for Santa Laws
Carpenters wish for Santa Saws

But up in my bedroom, behind closed doors
I'm busy dreaming of Santa Snores.

John Coldwell